Observation Video Guide

for

Berk

Infants, Children, and Adolescents in Action

Sixth Edition

prepared by

Laura E. Berk
Illinois State University

Sara Harris
Illinois State University

Trisha Mann
Illinois State University

Boston   New York   San Francisco
Mexico City   Montreal   Toronto   London   Madrid   Munich   Paris
Hong Kong   Singapore   Tokyo   Cape Town   Sydney

ISBN-13: 978-0-205-54702-9
ISBN-10:   0-205-54702-8

Printed in the United States of America

10 9 8 7 6 5 4 3 2   11 10 09 08

CONTENTS

INTRODUCTION

Infants, Children, and Adolescents in Action—the Observation Program that accompanies your textbook—contains hundreds of segments specially selected to illustrate the many theories, concepts, and milestones of development you are about to study. This Observation Guide is designed to help you use the Observation Program in conjunction with the text to deepen your understanding of child development and apply what you have learned to everyday life.

USING THE OBSERVATION PROGRAM AND GUIDE

The Observation Program has six main sections, each of which corresponds to a major part of your textbook. Within each main section are subsections illustrating the content of particular chapters:

Section	Chapters
Foundations of Development	Chapters 2–4
Infancy and Toddlerhood	Chapters 5–7
Early Childhood	Chapters 8–10
Middle Childhood	Chapters 11–13
Adolescence	Chapters 14–16
Emerging Adulthood	Chapter 17

As you read each major part of your text, watch the associated section of the Observation Program. Then answer the questions and carry out the activities in the Observation Guide. Each section of the Observation Guide contains a brief summary of related observation segments and three types of learning experiences:

• **Mastering Course Content** These questions will assist you in using the Observation Program to master essential concepts and make course content more memorable. Answer them diligently, and you should do better on examinations. If you have difficulty with a particular question, refer to the textbook pages associated with it to review.

• **Building Connections** These exercises will help you use the Observation Program to see the interconnectedness among all aspects of development. Although each observation segment highlights a specific topic, every facet of development is related to others; the child grows as an integrated whole. The "Building Connections" section encourages you to review observation segments and many parts of the text, keeping in mind linkages among physical, cognitive, emotional, and social development as well as diverse contexts that support all aspects of children's functioning.

• **Applying Your Knowledge: Learning Activities** These activities involve observations and interviews of children, parents, and teachers; discussion with your classmates; and individual reflection, using segments of the Observation Program as a starting point. On pages 117 and 118, you will find some helpful suggestions for observing and interviewing young children.

Each section of the Observation Guide is conveniently designed with perforated pages so that it can be turned in as a course assignment.

GETTING READY: REVIEW OF BASIC CONCEPTS AND THEORIES

To make the most of the Observation Program, it is vital that you master basic concepts of development and the introduction to contemporary theories in Chapter 1 of your textbook. After reading Chapter 1, test your knowledge by answering the questions in this section. *Infants, Children, and Adolescents in Action* will revisit these concepts and theories as they reappear in later chapters of your textbook. Note that here, and throughout the Observation Guide, questions are page-referenced to chapter content so you can easily refer to the text should you need to review.

BASIC ISSUES

1. Match each theoretical approach with its description: (6-9)

_____ Regards development as taking place in distinct contexts.	A. Theory that emphasizes one course of development
_____ Views development as adding on more of the same types of skills.	B. Theory that emphasizes many courses of development
_____ Regards development as universal across individuals and cultures.	C. Continuous theory
_____ Views environment as the most important influence in development.	D. Discontinuous theory
_____ Regards development as taking place in stages.	E. Theory that stresses nature
_____ Views heredity as the most important influence in development.	F. Theory that stresses nurture

2. Define the concept of *stage,* and cite an example of behavior change that would fit this definition. (8)

A. _____

B. _____

3. True or False: In taking a stand on each of the three basic issues of child development, most modern theories recognize the importance of both sides. (9)

Resilient Children

A Biology and Environment box in Chapter 1 describes current findings on *resilience*—the ability to adapt effectively in the face of threats to development. Several children in the Observation Program fit the definition of resilience: (1) Kristin, a child with Down syndrome who underwent six surgeries to correct a heart defect during her first 3 years; (2) Cara, a child who experienced birth complications; (3) Jacob, a child born to teenage parents; (4) Emily, a child abandoned shortly after birth in the People's Republic of China and reared in an unstimulating orphanage until 18 months of age; and (5) Dylan and Jeremy, whose parents are divorced and whose father has custody; Jeremy has cerebral palsy.

4. Name and describe three factors that protect resilient children from adversity. (10)
A. _____
B. _____
C. _____

5. Research on resilience indicates that successful interventions must focus on two areas: (10)
A. _____
B. _____

After you have observed Kristen, Cara, Jacob, Emily, Dylan, and Jeremy, be prepared to use this information to explain each child's capacity to overcome stressful life events.

CONTEMPORARY THEORIES

A variety of contemporary theoretical perspectives are illustrated in the Observation Program. These include: Piaget's cognitive-developmental theory; information processing; developmental cognitive neuroscience; ethology and evolutionary developmental psychology; ecological systems theory; Vygotsky's sociocultural theory; and the dynamic systems perspective.

Piaget's Cognitive-Developmental Theory

6. Describe Jean Piaget's view of child development. (18)

_____

_____

7. Match each of Piaget's stages with the appropriate description: (20)

_____ Thinking becomes abstract.	A. Preoperational
_____ Acting on the world with eyes, ears, hands, and mouth is the chief characteristic of this stage.	B. Concrete operational
	C. Formal operational
_____ Development of representation, including language and make-believe play, flourishes.	D. Sensorimotor
_____ Reasoning becomes logical and better organized.	

8. Describe three major contributions of Piaget's theory. (19–20)

A. _____

B. _____

C. _____

9. Cite two recent challenges to Piaget's theory. (20)

A. _____

B. _____

Information Processing

10. According to the *information-processing approach,* the human mind is best viewed as _____
_____. (21)

11. Explain how computers and flowcharts are used by information-processing theorists. (21)

_____

_____

_____

12. In what basic way are information processing and Piaget's theory alike? In what basic way are they different? (22)

A. _____

B. _____

13. Cite a major strength of the information-processing approach. (22)

_____

14. Describe two limitations of the information-processing approach. (22)

A. _____

B. _____

Developmental Cognitive Neuroscience

15. Describe *developmental cognitive neuroscience,* and provide an example of a research question that neuroscientists might tackle. (23)
A. _____
_____
B. _____

16. In what areas are neuroscientists making rapid progress? (23)
_____
_____

Ethology and Evolutionary Developmental Psychology

17. What is the focus of *ethology*? (23) _____
_____
_____

18. What is meant by *imprinting?* How have findings on imprinting been applied to child development? (23)
A. _____
B. _____

19. What is meant by a *sensitive period,* and how does it differ from a *critical period?* (23)
_____
_____

20. What is the primary focus of *evolutionary developmental psychology?* (24)
_____
_____

Vygotsky's Sociocultural Theory

21. Describe Vygotsky's *sociocultural theory.* (24)
_____
_____
_____

22. True or False: Both Piaget and Vygotsky viewed cognitive development as a socially mediated process. (25)

23. According to Vygotsky, children learn culturally valued skills through: (24–25)

_____ A. discovering how to perform them on their own.

_____ B. the guidance of more expert partners.

Ecological Systems Theory

24. Summarize the view of child development in *ecological systems theory*. (25)

_____

_____

25. Match each environmental level of ecological systems theory with the appropriate description or example: (26–27)

_____ Relationship between the child's home and school	A. Exosystem
_____ The influence of cultural values	B. Mesosystem
_____ The parent's workplace	C. Macrosystem
_____ The dynamic, ever-changing nature of the child's environment	D. Chronosystem
_____ The child's interaction with parents	E. Microsystem

26. Why is the person–environment system ever changing? (27)

_____

_____

New Directions: Development as a Dynamic System

27. A new wave of theorists has adopted a *dynamic systems perspective* on development. How do dynamic systems theorists view development? (27)

_____

_____

28. Why have researchers been attracted to this new view? (28)

_____

_____

CHAPTERS 2–4
BIOLOGICAL AND ENVIRONMENTAL FOUNDATIONS, PRENATAL DEVELOPMENT, AND BIRTH AND THE NEWBORN BABY

PARTICIPANTS

Child	Age	To identify on DVD, look for …
Anna Marie	2 weeks	White long-sleeved shirt and diaper, white socks
Cara	6 weeks	White, short-sleeved suit, bare legs and feet
Mac	3 months	Red shirt, blue overalls
Alex	5 months	Green playsuit
Nicole	11 months	White bow in hair, pink and white playsuit
Kristin	3½ years	White bow in hair, plaid playsuit

• Steve and Tonya, who were in their twenties when 3½-year-old Kristin, who has Down syndrome, was born; Nicole, their young daughter, who is 11 months old
• Gina and Lindrey, a young couple experiencing the birth of their second child using a natural childbirth method
• Adena and Cooper, new parents of Charlie, 4 months

SUMMARY

This section of the Observation Program contains three parent interviews:

(1) Steve and Tonya faced a tragedy rare among couples in their twenties. Their first child, Kristin, was born with Down syndrome. Steve and Tonya describe their reaction to Kristin's birth and how they adjusted to caring for a baby with serious disabilities and health problems.

(2) Gina and Lindrey experience the birth of their second child. After having her first baby by cesarean section, Gina is determined to have a vaginal delivery with her second. Her husband, Lindrey, describes the experience as Gina progresses through labor and delivery.

(3) Adena and Cooper discuss the transition to parenthood. Their son, Charlie, is 4 months old. The section concludes with newborn reflexes, which help ensure that the baby will survive and receive care and attention from adults.

MASTERING COURSE CONTENT

Chapter 2

BIOLOGICAL AND ENVIRONMENTAL FOUNDATIONS

Interview with Tonya and Steve

1. Kristin was born with Down syndrome, the (most/least) common chromosomal abnormality. It occurs in 1 out of every _____ live births. (60)

2. Kristin has the most frequent form of Down syndrome: *trisomy 21*. Describe how she inherited it. (60)

_____

_____

3. In what ways are Kristin's physical features typical of Down syndrome? How about her health problems? (61)

A. _____

_____

B. _____

_____

4. Cite the risk of having a child with Down syndrome for mothers, like Tonya, who bear children in their mid-twenties. (61) _____

How about mothers in their mid-thirties? _____

Mothers in their mid-forties? _____

5. The incidence of Down syndrome (rises/declines) dramatically with maternal age. Cite two explanations for this trend. (61)

A. _____

_____

B. _____

_____

6. True or False: Some studies suggest that Down syndrome and other chromosomal abnormalities are related to advanced paternal age. (61)

7. Why are infants with Down syndrome more difficult to care for than normal infants? According to Tonya, how has the family's second child, Nicole, contributed to Kristin's development? (61)

A. _____

_____

B. _____

_____

Mastering Course Content (continued)

8. The concept of *range of reaction* illustrates how heredity and environment work together to affect development. How has Down syndrome affected Kristin's range of reaction to environmental influences? (85)

_____

_____

_____

9. Using the recently expanded notion of *canalization,* explain why it was important to treat Kristin's health problems and provide her with an enriched environment at the earliest possible age. (86)

_____

_____

_____

10. The concept of *epigenesis* helps us understand how good parenting and early intervention can enhance Kristin's gene expression and, thereby, her hereditary potential. Explain how this is so. (88)

_____

_____

_____

Chapters 3 and 4

PRENATAL DEVELOPMENT AND BIRTH

Gina and Lindrey

11. When Gina and Lindrey arrived at the hospital, Gina's contractions were about five minutes apart. Gina was in Stage _____ of labor. (131)

12. Social support is important to the success of natural childbirth techniques. Give two examples of social support that Gina received during her labor. What research findings underscore the importance of social support during the childbirth process? (134)

A. _____

B. _____

C. _____

_____

Mastering Course Content (continued)

13. What medical intervention did Gina receive at the hospital? Explain why this instrument is used, including the controversy over its use. (136)

A. _____

B. _____

_____

_____

14. Why did Gina have her first child by *cesarean delivery?* What accounts for the worldwide rise in cesarean deliveries? (138)

A. _____

B. _____

Interview with Adena and Cooper

15. Adena and Cooper comment that it is difficult to tell what Charlie's temperament is like since he seems to change from one day to the next. Can personality be predicted using prenatal measures? Explain. (103)

_____

_____

_____

16. What stressors did Adena and Cooper encounter during the first few months of Charlie's life? How did they cope with these stressors? (157–158)

A. _____

_____

B. _____

_____

17. Under what circumstances is the transition to parenthood especially challenging? What interventions are available to high-risk parents? (158–159, 161)

A. _____

_____

B. _____

_____

Mastering Course Content (continued)

Chapter 4

THE NEWBORN BABY'S CAPACITIES

Newborn Reflexes

18. Anna Marie, Cara, Mac, and Alex illustrate a variety of newborn reflexes. After watching the demonstrations, briefly describe the adaptive function of each: (148)
Rooting: _____
Sucking: _____
Eye blink: _____
Babinski: _____
Moro: _____
Palmar grasp: _____
Tonic neck: _____
Crawling: _____
Stepping: _____
Escape: _____

19. Your textbook reviews only some of the newborn reflexive capacities. Which of the reflexes listed above are *not* included in your text? (148) _____
_____

20. Why did Professor Berk decide to illustrate reflexive capacities with babies no older than 5 months? (148) _____
_____
_____

Newborn States

21. List and briefly describe the five states of arousal that infants move in and out of during the first few weeks of life. (150)
A. _____
_____
B. _____
_____
C. _____
_____
D. _____
_____
E. _____
_____

Mastering Course Content (continued)

22. Watch as Art tries to calm crying Cara by holding her upright, close to his body. What other techniques are commonly used to soothe a crying baby? (153)

_____

_____

_____

23. Using examples from the video, cite examples of babies' responsiveness to touch, taste, smell, sound, and visual stimulation. (153–156)

_____

_____

_____

_____

_____

_____

BUILDING CONNECTIONS

Chapters 2, 3, and 4

1. According to ecological systems theory (see Chapter 1, page 27), children's environments are not static, but ever-changing. How did the arrival of Kristin's younger sister, Nicole, change Kristin's social environment in ways important for her development?

_____

_____

_____

_____

_____

2. Steve and Tonya comment that Kristin's physical problems at birth meant they had to learn to take care of her. How might illness and delayed development influence the quality of caregiving a child receives? What factors—within the family and the surrounding environment—probably helped Steve and Tonya in providing Kristin with the affection and stimulation she needed to develop favorably? (See Chapter 1, pages 26–27 for help in answering this question.)

_____

_____

_____

_____

3. Gina and Lindrey's story provides a look at the natural childbirth experience from the parents' point of view. Consider for a moment what childbirth must be like for the infant. Describe aspects of the infant's experience during labor, explaining how babies are equipped to handle the trauma of childbirth. (130–132)

_____

_____

_____

_____

_____

_____

4. Adena and Cooper's relationship has remained strong and positive after the birth of their baby. Cite at least one factor that probably eased the transition to parenthood for Adena and Cooper. (158–159) _____

_____

_____

_____

APPLYING YOUR KNOWLEDGE: LEARNING ACTIVITIES

Chapters 2, 3, and 4

1. Tonya comments that "she was not prepared at all" and "was devastated" to learn that her newborn daughter had Down syndrome. Using ecological systems theory (Chapter 1, pages 26-27), design a hospital intervention program to help new parents adapt to the birth of a baby like Kristin. Keep in mind the importance of bidirectional influences between parent and child, social support, and connections between microsystems (such as home and hospital).

_____
_____
_____
_____
_____
_____
_____
_____
_____
_____
_____
_____
_____
_____

2. Ask a young couple who have recently become parents about satisfactions and concerns that accompany new parenthood. What factors are likely to make parenting easier? What factors might make it more difficult?

_____
_____
_____
_____
_____
_____
_____
_____
_____
_____
_____
_____
_____

Applying Your Knowledge: Learning Activities (continued)

3. Women's childbirth experiences vary greatly. Interview the mother of a small child about her labor and delivery experience. Compare and contrast the experience with the childbirth segment in the Observation Program. What childbirth method was used for labor and delivery? Were there any medical interventions or birth complications? Was social support available? Explain.

_____

_____

_____

_____

_____

_____

_____

_____

_____

_____

CHAPTERS 5–7

INFANCY AND TODDLERHOOD

PARTICIPANTS

Child	Age	To identify on DVD, look for …
Anna Marie	2 weeks	White long-sleeved shirt and diaper, white socks
Cara	6 weeks	White, short-sleeved suit, bare legs and feet; later pink sleeper
Mac	3 months	Red shirt, blue overalls
Alex	5 months	Green playsuit
Hannah	7 months	Pink bow on head, multicolored playsuit with pink top
Randy	8 months	Yellow shirt, white jumpsuit
Nicole	11 months	White bow in hair, pink and white playsuit
Bailey	12 months	Red shirt, plaid overalls
Braxton	15 months	White shirt, black pants
Katherine	18 months	Blue shirt, blue striped overalls
Luke	20 months	Gray shirt, black pants
Ben	21 months	White print shirt, tan pants
Zachary	23 months	Green, black, and white striped shirt
Sophie	2½ years	Purple shirt and pants
Elena	2½ years	Denim jumper
Kristin	3½ years	White bow in hair, plaid playsuit
Zacharie	4 years	White shirt, black pants

CHAPTER 5
PHYSICAL DEVELOPMENT IN INFANCY
AND TODDLERHOOD

SUMMARY

This section of the Observation Program includes segments on physical development, beginning with changes in body size, proportions, and muscle–fat makeup during infancy and toddlerhood. Next, the attainment of motor skills is addressed, along with factors that influence these milestones and their implications for other aspects of development. Early learning— classical and operant conditioning, habituation and recovery, and newborn imitation—is also illustrated, followed by depth perception and its intimate relationship to motor development.

MASTERING COURSE CONTENT

BODY GROWTH

Compare the body size, proportions, and body fat of Anna Marie, Cara, Alex, and Katherine. Then answer the following questions:

1. Five-month-old Alex has accumulated considerably more body fat than 2-week-old Anna Marie and 6-week-old Cara. What is taking place in brain growth over the first two years that is supported by the high fat content of human milk? (166–167)

A. _____

B. _____

2. At 18 months, Katherine is losing her babyish appearance. What is happening to Katherine's growth that makes her look more like a little girl than a baby? (167)

_____

3. The narrator notes, "At first the head and chest have a growth advantage, but the trunk and legs gradually pick up speed." What growth trend is being described? (167)

_____

4. Alex's father commented off-camera that Alex is a "good eater." In contrast, 21-month-old Ben's appetite has lessened and he is becoming pickier about the foods he eats. How is this change in quantity of food eaten related to body growth? Explain why young children's wariness of new foods may be adaptive. (304)

A. _____

_____

B. _____

_____

LEARNING CAPACITIES

5. Two-week-old Anna Marie demonstrates *classical conditioning* during feeding. Identify each of the components of classical conditioning in this example. (183–184)

unconditioned stimulus (UCS): _____

unconditioned response (UCR): _____

conditioned stimulus (CS): _____

conditioned response (CR): _____

Mastering Course Content (continued)

6. Anna Marie's sucking can easily be classically conditioned. Other responses, such as fear, are more difficult to classically condition in young babies. Explain why. (184)

_____

_____

7. Professor Berk and Mac illustrate *operant conditioning.* What stimulus serves as a reinforcer for Mac, increasing the probability that he will smile again? _____
What stimulus serves as a reinforcer for Professor Berk, increasing the probability that she will smile again? (184) _____

8. Cara habituates to the green ring and then recovers to the yellow ring. These responses indicate that Cara (can/cannot) remember the green ring and (can/cannot) distinguish the green from the yellow ring perceptually. (185)

9. Describe the current debate over the capacities that underlie newborn imitation, such as Anna Marie's imitation of Professor Berk's mouth opening. (186–187)

_____

_____

MOTOR DEVELOPMENT

10. According to *dynamic systems theory of motor development,* mastery of motor skills involves acquiring increasingly complex systems of action. Explain what this means, and describe examples from the Observation Program. (189)

A. _____

B. _____

11. The dynamic systems theory of motor development regards each new skill as a joint product of four factors: (189)

A. _____

B. _____

C. _____

D. _____

12. Explain how the motor capacities of 21-month-old Ben, who plays ball with Professor Berk, foster cognitive and social development. (187–189)

_____

_____

Mastering Course Content (continued)

13. Kristin's early experiences slowed her rate of motor development and also changed its form. In what way were her experiences similar to those of the Iranian babies observed by Wayne Dennis? (190) _____

_____

_____

14. Of all motor skills, _____ may play the greatest role in infant cognitive development. (190)

15. Look closely at 7-month-old Hannah. Cite an example of how gross motor development supports improvement in fine motor skills. (190)

_____

_____

PERCEPTUAL DEVELOPMENT

16. How does the behavior of Anna Marie, Cara, Hannah, and Nicole illustrate research findings on infants' sound perception? (193–194)
A. Responsiveness to the human voice (Anna Marie): _____

_____

_____

_____

B. Responsiveness to sound patterns (Cara, Hannah, and Nicole): _____

_____

_____

_____

_____

17. According to Eleanor and James Gibson's *differentiation theory,* perception is guided by discovery of *affordances.* What does this mean? How do motor skills affect Alex, Hannah, Bailey, and Braxton's different views of action possibilities a drop-off affords? (202–203)
A. _____

B. _____

C. _____

_____

18. Explain how crawling promotes sensitivity to depth information. (196–197)

_____

_____

BUILDING CONNECTIONS

Chapter 5

1. Although 5-month-old Alex has accumulated body fat, his stepping reflex is plainly evident. Why does adding body fat usually lead the stepping reflex to disappear by age 2 months? Alex enjoys being upright and jumping. Describe research indicating that these experiences might have contributed to his retention of the stepping response. (148)

A. _____

_____

_____

B. _____

_____

_____

_____

2. Because of her early experiences, Kristin scoots instead of crawling. Observe Kristin's scooting again. How will scooting likely affect Kristin's exploration? Do you think Kristin's scooting contributed to the fact that at age 3, she has not yet begun to walk on her own? Explain.

_____

_____

_____

_____

_____

_____

3. As the text notes, researchers believe that crawling is so important in structuring babies' experience of the world that it may promote a new level of brain organization. Look ahead to Chapters 6 and 7. Note cognitive and emotional milestones that emerge around the same time as crawling, and record them below.

Cognitive (Chapter 6, Table 6.2):_____

_____

_____

Emotional (Chapter 7, pages 253–259):_____

_____

_____

_____

4. Using examples from the Observation Program and your text, cite factors that contribute to early physical development. Explain how physical growth is a canalized process. (86)

A. _____

_____

B. _____

_____

APPLYING YOUR KNOWLEDGE: LEARNING ACTIVITIES

Chapter 5

1. Parental beliefs about infant development vary from culture to culture. Some parents think that training children in motor skills is essential. Others believe that no special training or practice is necessary. Ask two or three parents, preferably of different ethnic backgrounds, to describe how they support the motor development of their babies. How important does each parent think it is to encourage crawling, standing, walking, and other motor milestones? To what extent do you think culture plays a role in their responses?

_____

_____

_____

_____

_____

_____

_____

_____

_____

_____

_____

2. Perception and action are intimately related. Observe an infant or toddler at play for 15 minutes and record the child's gross and fine motor skills. Explain how the child's experiences in moving about independently and manipulating objects contribute to (a) pattern perception, (b) depth perception, (c) object perception, and (d) intermodal perception.

A. _____

_____

B. _____

_____

_____

C. _____

_____

_____

D. _____

_____

_____

CHAPTER 6
COGNITIVE DEVELOPMENT IN INFANCY
AND TODDLERHOOD

SUMMARY

Segments on infant cognitive development trace mastery of object permanence during Piaget's sensorimotor stage, along with advances in mental representation during the second year, as illustrated by make-believe play and categorization. Then the Observation Program turns to early language development. Prelinguistic milestones are depicted, with emphasis on infant receptivity to language and characteristics of parental communication that help infants make sense of a complex speech stream. Alex, Hannah, Zachary, Katherine, and Nicole demonstrate early communicative capacities, first words, and the distinction between language comprehension and production. Zachary and Ben highlight individual differences in early styles of language learning. The section ends with examples of how storybook reading and make-believe play foster early language development.

MASTERING COURSE CONTENT

PIAGET'S COGNITIVE-DEVELOPMENTAL THEORY:
THE SENSORIMOTOR STAGE

1. The narrator comments, "In the early months of life, infants have some understanding of *object permanence*." Describe research evidence that supports this claim. (210–211)

_____

_____

2. If 5-month-old Alex has some understanding of object permanence, what explains his failure to search for a hidden object? (212–213)

_____

_____

3. List three object-hiding tasks in order of difficulty, and indicate whether 8-month-old Randy, 12-month-old Bailey, and 18-month-old Katherine master them at typical ages. (212–213)

A. _____ Randy: _____
B. _____ Bailey: _____
C. _____ Katherine: _____

Mastering Course Content (continued)

4. Eighteen-month-old Katherine feeds a baby doll, and 21-month-old Ben talks on the telephone. According to Piaget, in which sensorimotor substage does make-believe play emerge? What cognitive capacity supports its development? (211–212, 215)

A. _____

_____

B. _____

_____

5. Watch the make-believe interaction between Professor Berk and 23-month-old Zachary during the tea party. How is Professor Berk *scaffolding* Zachary's current level of ability? What are the benefits of adult involvement in young children's pretending? (227, 229)

A. _____

_____

B. _____

_____

LANGUAGE DEVELOPMENT

6. Briefly describe the behaviorist and nativist perspectives on language development. For each, note supportive evidence and limitations. (237–239)

Behaviorist: _____

_____

Supportive evidence: _____

_____

Limitations: _____

_____

Nativist: _____

_____

Supportive evidence: _____

_____

Limitations: _____

_____

7. Describe two types of *interactionist theories* of language development, noting limitations and unresolved issues related to each. (239–240)

A. _____

_____

B. _____

_____

Mastering Course Content (continued)

8. Cite at least two examples from the Observation Program that illustrate the joint contribution of inner predispositions and environmental inputs to language development. (237–240)

A. _____

_____

B. _____

_____

9. Listen to Hannah's babbling. Cite two ways in which babbling paves the way for language. (240–241)

A. _____

B. _____

10. Seven-month-old Hannah establishes *joint attention* with her mother, who comments on what Hannah sees. Explain how joint attention contributes to early language development. (241)

_____

_____

11. Watch as Zachary points and then adds the word "ball." What is Zachary's pointing called, and why is it important? (242)

A. _____

B. _____

12. One of 23-month-old Zachary's first words is "ball." What makes this a typical word in children's early vocabularies? (242)

_____

_____

13. Nicole and Zachary illustrate how language comprehension is ahead of production. Explain why. (243) _____

_____

14. Listen as 7-month-old Hannah's mother, Connie, speaks to her. What term is used to describe the form of language Connie uses? List characteristics of this form of language, and explain why adults use it when talking to infants. (245)

A. _____

B. _____

_____

Mastering Course Content (continued)

15. The text points out that parents constantly fine-tune their child-directed speech, adjusting the length and content of their utterances to fit with children's needs. Note how 18-month-old Katherine's parents interact with her. How does their communication differ from that of 7-month-old Hannah's mother? (245) _____

_____

_____

_____

_____

_____

16. As you watch Luke, Sophie, and Elena read storybooks with their mothers, explain how storybook reading fosters early language development. (244–245)

_____

_____

_____

_____

BUILDING CONNECTIONS

Chapter 6

1. Review the milestones of gross and fine motor development (see Chapter 5, page 188). Cite examples of how motor attainments support the development of cognition and language during the first two years, drawing on infants' and toddlers' behavior in the Observation Program.

Cognition:_____

_____

_____

_____

_____

Language:_____

_____

_____

_____

_____

2. Look ahead to Chapter 7, pages 273–274, and read the section on quality of caregiving and security of attachment. Next, review parents communicating with their babies in the Observation Program. How does child-directed speech contribute to the development of a secure attachment bond? _____

_____

_____

_____

_____

_____

3. Cite characteristics of make-believe play that Sophie and Elena demonstrate. Explain how their mother facilitates make-believe while also supporting the twins' language development. (229, 244–246) _____

_____

_____

_____

APPLYING YOUR KNOWLEDGE: LEARNING ACTIVITIES

Chapter 6

1. Try the object-hiding tasks illustrated in the Observation Program with four infants and toddlers, one from each of the following age ranges: 5-8 months, 8-12 months, 12-18 months, and 18-24 months. Describe each child's behavior, and indicate whether your observations support Piaget's developmental sequence of object permanence. (To review the object-hiding tasks, consult Chapter 6, pages 211-214.)

5- to 8-month-old: _____
_____
_____

8- to 12-month-old: _____
_____
_____

12- to 18-month-old: _____
_____
_____

18- to 24-month-old: _____
_____
_____

2. Interview a parent of a child between 18 and 24 months of age, asking for a list of the words the child produces and the contexts in which each is used. Look for illustrations of the sensorimotor foundations of early language, the gradual acceleration with age in the number of words learned, and first two-word combinations.

_____
_____
_____
_____
_____
_____
_____
_____
_____

Applying Your Knowledge: Learning Activities (continued)

3. When you next have an opportunity, describe the form and content of the utterances of two adults (one man and one woman) as they interact with infants and toddlers. (Shopping malls, grocery stores, and city parks are good places to observe.) Next, listen to yourself speaking to a baby. To what extent did the communication of each adult reflect the characteristics of child-directed speech? _____

_____

_____

_____

_____

_____

_____

_____

_____

_____

_____

_____

_____

_____

CHAPTER 7

EMOTIONAL AND SOCIAL DEVELOPMENT IN INFANCY AND TODDLERHOOD

SUMMARY

Emotional milestones of infancy—the social smile, laughter, fear (including stranger anxiety), use of the caregiver as a secure base, and social referencing—are illustrated in this section of the Observation Program. Variations in temperament are explored by examining individual differences in sociability, attention span, activity level, and persistence, as well as the importance of adapting parenting to children's temperaments. Next, the development of infant–caregiver attachment is considered. Among the milestones depicted are newborn capacities that evoke loving care; emotional responsiveness to the familiar caregiver in the first half-year; appearance of clear-cut attachment (including separation anxiety) around 6 to 8 months; and the capacity to tolerate short absences of the parent by the end of the second year. The vital role of sensitive, responsive caregiving in the development of a secure attachment bond is explained. Similarities and differences in mothers' and fathers' styles of interacting with their babies are also shown.

Finally, a secure attachment bond fosters a sturdy sense of self. Emergence of self-recognition is explored by dabbing red dye on toddlers' noses and observing reactions to their changed appearance using a mirror. Early self-development provides the foundation for compliance and self-control, which emerge during the second year of life. First, 1½-year-old Luke illustrates the toddler's ability to comply with adult directives, followed by 2½-year-old Sophie and Elena, who demonstrate self-control during a delay-of-gratification task.

MASTERING COURSE CONTENT

EMOTIONAL DEVELOPMENT

1. Review the images of Zachary, Alex, Randy, Ben, Nicole, and Kristin at the beginning of this section. Describe the emotion each expresses, and indicate how that emotion helps organize and regulate behavior. (254–256)

Zachary (with jack-in-the-box): _____

_____

Alex (watching toy): _____

_____

Randy (watching Ben): _____

_____

Ben (playing ball): _____

_____

Kristin and Nicole (playing ball): _____

_____

2. What is the major emotional milestone that emerges between 6 and 10 weeks of age? What is its function? (255)

A. _____

B. _____

3. Describe the events that make 7-month-old Hannah and 23-month-old Zachary laugh. How do the two events differ? What explains this age-related change in the circumstances that evoke laughter? (255)

Hannah: _____

_____

Zachary: _____

_____

_____

4. When do fear reactions appear in infancy, and why are they adaptive? (256)

_____

_____

5. Eight-month-old Randy displays *stranger anxiety*. What three factors affect an infant's fear of unfamiliar adults? (256)

A. _____

B. _____

C. _____

Mastering Course Content (continued)

6. What is meant by a *secure base?* What behaviors indicate that Randy uses Sheryl as a secure base? (256)

A. _____

B. _____

_____

7. Randy engages in *social referencing.* Explain this behavior, and indicate why it develops by the end of the first year. (257) _____

_____

_____

8. What does social referencing reveal about infants' emotional understanding? (257)

_____

_____

DEVELOPMENT OF TEMPERAMENT

9. One way of assessing temperament is through direct observation. Describe behaviors of children in the Observation Program that suggest the following temperamental characteristics (260–261):

Note: To observe Stephen and Alison, you will need to fast-forward to the Early Childhood section of the video.

Shy (Zachary): _____

_____

Sociable (Katherine): _____

_____

Attentive (Stephen and Alison): _____

_____

Distractible (Zacharie): _____

_____

Inactive, cautious (Stephen and Alison): _____

_____

Active, willing to take risks (Zacharie): _____

_____

Persistent (Zachary): _____

_____

Easily frustrated (Braxton): _____

_____

Mastering Course Content (continued)

10. As you observe children interacting with their parents, are there any noticeable sex differences in temperament? Explain. (264)

_____

_____

_____

11. Explain *goodness-of-fit.* How does Joanna's enthusiastic response to Braxton's success with the box of shapes create a "good fit" with his temperament? (266–267)

A. _____

B. _____

_____

DEVELOPMENT OF ATTACHMENT

12. Observe 2-week-old Anna Marie, 6-week-old Cara, 5-month-old Alex, and 7-month-old Hannah interacting with their caregivers. For each, describe behaviors that serve to keep the caregiver nearby. (269–270)

Anna Marie: _____

_____

Cara: _____

_____

Alex: _____

_____

Hannah: _____

_____

13. According to Bowlby, the development of attachment takes place in four phases. Note behaviors of Anna Marie, Alex, Hannah, and Katherine that reveal the phase of attachment each child has reached. (269–270)

The preattachment phase:

Child: _____   Behaviors: _____

_____

The "attachment-in-the-making" phase:

Child: _____   Behaviors: _____

_____

The phase of "clear-cut" attachment:

Child: _____   Behaviors: _____

_____

Formation of a reciprocal relationship:

Child: _____   Behaviors: _____

_____

Mastering Course Content (continued)

14. According to your text and the Observation Program, _____ caregiving supports the development of attachment. Describe caregiving behaviors of parents in the Observation Program that foster attachment security. (273–274)

_____

_____

_____

15. Watch parents interacting with their infants and toddlers at the end of this section. How do mothers and fathers differ? Are fathers at a disadvantage when developing an attachment bond with their infants? Explain, citing research in the text. (276, 278–279)

_____

_____

_____

_____

16. The narrator comments that attachment has far-reaching consequences for children's development. Describe research that supports this statement. (281–282)

_____

_____

_____

SELF-DEVELOPMENT

17. Compare the reactions of 11-month-old Nicole, 23-month-old Zachary, and 3-year-old Kristin to their changed appearance in a mirror. What behaviors indicate that Zachary and Kristin clearly recognize themselves? (283–284)

_____

_____

_____

18. The narrator comments that noticing the contrast between reactions of the physical world, the social world, and their own movements may help infants and toddlers build an image of self as separate from external reality. Explain what this means. (284)

_____

_____

_____

19. Why is the development of self-control especially important in the first few years of life? (285–286) _____

_____

_____

Mastering Course Content (continued)

20. What cognitive capacities permit 20-month-old Luke to comply with his mother's request to bring her the ball? (285) _____
_____
_____

21. Although Luke can comply, he is also capable of saying "No!" For children who experience warm, sensitive caregiving and reasonable expectations for mature behavior, should toddlerhood be called "the terrible twos?" Why or why not? (285–286) _____
_____
_____
_____

22. During the delay of gratification task, what strategies do Sophie and Elena use to help themselves wait? (285–286) _____
_____
_____

BUILDING CONNECTIONS

Chapter 7

1. Review the milestones of gross and fine motor development on page 188 in Chapter 5. Cite examples of how motor attainments support the development of cognition and language during the first two years, drawing on infants' and toddlers' behavior in the Observation Program.
Cognition: _____

_____

_____

Language: _____

_____

_____

2. How do the social smiles of 6-week-old Cara and 5-month-old Alex parallel the development of infant perceptual capacities—in particular, babies' increasing sensitivity to visual patterns, including the human face? (See Chapter 5, pages 195-196, 199–200.) _____

_____

_____

_____

_____

3. Recall from Chapter 6 (pages 242–243) that toddlers typically experience a vocabulary spurt between 18 months and 2 years of age. During this time, they also show rapid gains in self-control, as measured by delay of gratification (pages 285–286). How might the acquisition of language contribute to the development of self-control? _____

_____

_____

_____

_____

_____

_____

_____

_____

4. Chapters 5 through 7 of your text include numerous examples of how parenting contributes to diverse aspects of physical, cognitive, and emotional and social development. Describe parent behaviors in the Observation Program that support favorable development in infancy and toddlerhood. _____

_____

_____

_____

_____

_____

APPLYING YOUR KNOWLEDGE: LEARNING ACTIVITIES

Chapter 7

1. The text indicates that signs of almost all the basic emotions—happiness, interest, surprise, fear, anger, sadness, and disgust—are present in early infancy (see pages 254–256). Review earlier segments of the Observation Program, and carefully observe the facial, body, and vocal expressions of infants of different ages. Record instances of the basic emotions listed above, and compare younger with older babies.

Anna Marie (2 weeks): _____

_____

Cara (6 weeks): _____

_____

Mac (3 months): _____

_____

Alex (5 months): _____

_____

Hannah (7 months): _____

_____

Randy (8 months): _____

_____

Nicole (11 months): _____

_____

Do emotional expressions seem to become better organized and more recognizable with age? Explain. _____

_____

_____

2. Review the section on the beginnings of emotional self-regulation in the text (see pages 258–259). Return to the Observation Program, and watch mothers and fathers interacting with their infants. Select two examples, and describe how each parent fosters emotional self-regulation. Pay particular attention to the pace of the parents' behavior in relation to the baby's needs.

A. _____

_____

_____

_____

_____

B. _____

_____

_____

_____

_____

Applying Your Knowledge: Learning Activities (continued)

3. Arrange to visit a child-care center during early morning hours when parents bring their infants and toddlers for the day. What steps do the staff take to ease the stress of separation from the parent? How do children greet their caretakers? Describe several examples, and indicate whether children seem, for the most part, securely attached to professional caregivers. On the basis of information provided in the Applying What We Know table on page 234, rate the overall quality of the child-care center as excellent, average, or poor. Is overall quality related to sensitive, responsive care? Explain.

Steps staff take to ease separation anxiety: _____

_____

_____

_____

_____

Children's reaction to caregivers: _____

_____

_____

_____

_____

_____

Quality of attachment to professional caregivers: _____

_____

_____

_____

_____

Overall quality of the child-care center: _____ excellent _____ average _____ poor
Relationship of center quality to sensitive, responsive care: _____

_____

_____

_____

_____

CHAPTERS 8–10

EARLY CHILDHOOD

PARTICIPANTS

Child	Age	To identify on DVD, look for …
Emily	3 years	Pink, blue, and green striped dress
Alison	4 years	Blond hair, green dress
Emily	4 years	White blouse, pink and purple patterned jumper
Matthew	4 years	Red hair, glasses
Zacharie	4 years	White shirt with pictures of tractors
Stephen	4½ years	Brown shirt with picture of deer, brown pants
Claire	5 years	Blond hair, pink dress
Janaisa	5 years	Denim jumper, braids
Justin	6 years	Green shirt
Liesl	7 years	Long dark hair, white and flowered shirt
Zoe	7 years	Light blue T-shirt

• Preschool and kindergarten children at Thomas Metcalf Laboratory School and the Child Care Center, Illinois State University
• Joanna, 26-year-old single mother of Zacharie, age 4, and Braxton, age 15 months
• Jane, 38-year-old adoptive single mother of Emily, 3 years, from China
• Bill, a 24-year-old divorcé and custodial parent of two children: Dylan, age 5, and Jeremy, age 4, who has cerebral palsy
• Deb and Ron, in their mid-thirties, dual-earner parents of Charlie, age 4, and Maggie, age 1

CHAPTERS 8 AND 9
PHYSICAL AND COGNITIVE DEVELOPMENT
IN EARLY CHILDHOOD

SUMMARY

This section opens with an overview of the motor accomplishments of early childhood. Young children's mastery of motor skills through everyday play rather than formal instruction is emphasized.

The Observation Program then turns to cognitive development, showing how gains in representation, as illustrated by language and make-believe play, support cognitive development in early childhood. Piaget's preoperational stage is demonstrated through children's performance on conservation and classification tasks. Vygotsky's sociocultural theory is depicted through images of children working on tasks within their zones of proximal development, engaging in private speech, and interacting with adults and peers in ways that promote the transfer of culturally adaptive strategies from more expert partners to the child.

Next, the Observation Program focuses on information processing as another approach to understanding children's thinking. As 4-year-old Stephen plays a memory game, he demonstrates that recognition develops ahead of recall. Larry and Linda's discussion of a recent trip to the zoo with Stephen and Alison shows that preschoolers' memory in everyday contexts is often excellent, particularly for unusual events. Seven-year-old Zoe's ability to predict where a puppet will look for Band-Aids reveals her understanding of false belief. Zoe also demonstrates gains that occur in middle childhood, as she successfully solves a second-order false-belief task. Preschoolers' and kindergarteners' play and conversations display remarkable attainments in vocabulary, grammar, and pragmatics of language. The applications of information processing to literacy are depicted through 4-year-old Matthew's rendition of the story of Little Red Riding Hood. In addition, children's acquisition of literacy and mathematical knowledge through play is examined.

MASTERING COURSE CONTENT

MOTOR DEVELOPMENT

Chapter 8

1. What changes in body growth pave the way for new motor skills involving large muscles of the body, such as running, jumping, and hopping? (294, 312)

_____

_____

2. Select one of the following gross motor skills, and describe how it improves over the preschool years: running, jumping, hopping, or throwing. (312) _____

_____

_____

_____

_____

_____

_____

3. Cite gains in fine motor development over the preschool years. (312–313)

_____

_____

_____

_____

_____

4. Describe sex differences in motor development during early childhood, including environmental factors that contribute to these differences. (317)

A. _____

_____

B. _____

_____

5. The narrator states that the appropriate goal of adult involvement in preschoolers' motor development should be fun rather than learning the correct technique. How should adults promote motor development during the preschool years? (317)

_____

_____

Mastering Course Content (continued)

6. Do adult pressure and an emphasis on competition foster advanced motor development in early childhood? Explain, citing research from the text. (317)

_____
_____
_____
_____
_____

COGNITIVE DEVELOPMENT

Chapter 9

Piaget's Preoperational Stage

7. Return to the Infancy and Toddlerhood section of the Observation Program and review 18-month-old Katherine's feeding of a baby doll and 21-month-old Ben's telephone play. Compare the make-believe of the two toddlers with that of Stephen and Alison, who are both 4 years old. Cite at least three ways in which Stephen's and Alison's pretending is more advanced than the toddlers'. (322–323)

A. _____
_____

B. _____
_____

C. _____
_____

8. Four-year-old Stephen gives a typical preoperational response to a conservation-of-liquid task. According to Piaget, which of the following aspects of thinking are indicated by Stephen's failure to conserve? (325–326)

_____ lack of object permanence   _____ egocentrism
_____ perception-bound thought   _____ irreversibility
_____ centration   _____ animistic thinking

9. Research shows that when tasks are made relevant to their everyday lives, preschoolers do better on Piagetian tasks than expected. How does 4-year-old Alison's performance on a conservation-of-mass problem illustrate this finding? (325, 327–328)

_____
_____
_____
_____

Mastering Course Content (continued)

10. When asked to categorize a set of objects in more than one way, 4-year-old Zacharie's performance illustrates the rigidity of preoperational thought. Compare Zacharie's approach to this task with that of 7-year-old Liesl. What does Liesl's performance reveal about her cognitive development? Explain. (326–329)

A. _____

_____

_____

B. _____

_____

_____

Vygotsky's Sociocultural Theory

11. Are any of Piaget's or Vygotsky's educational principles evident in the preschool and kindergarten classrooms? Explain, citing examples from the video. (332–333, 336)

_____

_____

_____

12. Several children in the Observation Program use *private speech*. What tasks are they working on, and why do these tasks evoke private speech? According to Vygotsky, what function does private speech serve? (333–334)

A. _____

_____

B. _____

_____

13. Describe the difference between Piaget's and Vygotsky's views on the development of private speech. Cite three research findings that favor Vygotsky's interpretation. (333–334) _____

_____

_____

A. _____

_____

B. _____

_____

C. _____

_____

Mastering Course Content (continued)

14. According to Vygotsky, to promote cognitive development, collaboration between children and more expert partners should take place on tasks within the *zone of proximal development.* How does 3-year-old Emily's mother create a zone of proximal development? (333–336) _____
_____
_____

15. Both Piaget and Vygotsky regarded children as _____ seekers of knowledge. However, their theories make different assumptions about how children learn. Briefly summarize these differences. (322, 332, 333–336)
Piaget: _____
_____
_____

Vygotsky: _____
_____
_____

Information Processing

16. Review Stephen's performance on the memory game again. Does Stephen group together items in an orderly fashion while playing the game? (*Hint:* You can determine this by observing the order in which he recalls the items.) If Stephen engages in item-grouping, do you think he does so intentionally? Why do preschoolers rarely use deliberate memory strategies, such as rehearsal and organization? (339–340)
A. _____
_____
B. _____
_____
C. _____
_____
D. _____
_____

17. Explain why Stephen's *recognition* in the memory game is considerably more accurate than his *recall*. What accounts for older children's more accurate *recall*? (339)
A. _____
_____
B. _____
_____

Mastering Course Content (continued)

18. Record the information that Stephen and Alison remember about a special one-time event—a trip to the zoo. Is their recall for everyday experiences likely to be better than their memory for listlike information? Explain your answer. (340)

A. _____

_____

_____

B. _____

_____

_____

19. In talking with their son and daughter about past events, how are Larry and Linda helping Stephen and Alison build an autobiographical memory? (340)

_____

_____

_____

_____

20. As Stephen and Alison get older, they will be unlikely to recall experiences that happened to them before age 3. What is this type of forgetting called? (224–225)

_____

According to current research, what two developmental milestones bring an end to this period of forgetting?

A. _____

_____

B. _____

_____

21. Why is Matthew's memory for the story of Little Red Riding Hood so rich and elaborate? What type of memory is Matthew demonstrating? (340)

A. _____

_____

B. _____

_____

22. What do Zoe's responses to Professor Berk reveal about her understanding of false belief? (342–344) _____

_____

_____

_____

_____

Mastering Course Content (continued)

23. Cite factors that contribute to the young child's theory of mind. (343–344) _____
_____
_____
_____
_____

Language Development

24. Using the kindergartner reading a story, the preschool boys conversing during block play, 5-year-old Josh "talking down" to his baby sister, and Alison's polite way of saying it's time to go, cite examples of gains in vocabulary, grammar, and pragmatics by the end of the preschool years.

Vocabulary (356–358): _____
_____
_____

Grammar (358–359): _____
_____
_____

Pragmatics (359–360): _____
_____
_____

25. Using examples of parents and teachers interacting with young children in the Observation Program, explain why adult–child conversation is so important for language development in early childhood (360–361)

_____
_____
_____
_____
_____

26. When talking to preschoolers, what techniques do sensitive, caring adults use that support language skills? (360)

_____
_____
_____
_____
_____

Mastering Course Content (continued)

Emergent Literacy and Mathematical Development

27. The narrator points out that literacy beings long before formal schooling. It builds on a broad foundation of spoken language, experience with literacy materials, and understanding of the world. How does the kindergarten recycling center promote early literacy development? (344, 346–347) _____

_____

_____

_____

_____

28. Availability of informal counting experiences in children's everyday lives promotes early number understanding. As kindergartners play in the recycling center, they reveal their grasp of basic mathematical principles. Name these principles, and describe the behaviors that illustrate each. (346) _____

_____

_____

_____

_____

29. Using examples from the video and research presented in your text, explain the benefits of incorporating play into early childhood programs. (350–351)

_____

_____

_____

_____

BUILDING CONNECTIONS

Chapters 8 and 9

1. Review the suggestions for enhancing early childhood motor development on page 317 in Chapter 8 and for enhancing literacy and mathematical knowledge on pages 346–348 in Chapter 9. What do the two sets of recommendations have in common?

_____
_____
_____
_____
_____
_____
_____
_____
_____
_____

2. Summarize the functions of make-believe play recognized by Piaget and Vygotsky (see Chapter 6, page 229; Chapter 9, pages 322–333). In view of these functions, how does make-believe support not just cognitive development but also emotional and social development? What role does make-believe play serve in the core knowledge perspective? How is this view different from the views of Piaget and Vygotsky?

A. _____
_____

B. _____
_____

C. _____
_____

D. _____
_____

3. When parents take time to talk about past experiences (as Larry and Linda did with Stephen and Alison), they help their children construct an autobiographical memory. What emotional and social competencies might they also be fostering through conversations about the past? (Chapter 6, pages 224–225; Chapter 9, pages 339–341)

_____
_____
_____
_____

Building Connections (continued)

4. Using examples from the video (children's responses to Piagetian tasks, Zoe's responses to false-belief tasks, and children's interactions in the recycling center), explain why Piaget's assertion that children are egocentric is inaccurate. (326–329)

_____
_____
_____
_____
_____
_____

5. Your text and the Observation Program emphasize that opportunities to converse with adults are consistently related to general measures of language progress. How might this finding help explain SES differences in intelligence test performance and academic achievement? (See pages 343–344 for a description of research findings relevant to this question.) _____

_____
_____
_____
_____

6. Adult–child communication is vital for language development. Using research on child care (Chapter 9, pages 350–351, 353–354) and language development (Chapter 9, pages 355–360), explain how group size, caregiver–child ratio, and teacher preparation are related to child-care quality. _____

_____
_____
_____
_____
_____

7. Referring to the _Applying What We Know_ tables on pages 350 and 354 of the text, compare the characteristics of a high-quality home life for preschoolers to those of developmentally appropriate early childhood programs. What features do they have in common? What competencies are emphasized in both the home and the school environment? _____

_____
_____
_____
_____
_____
_____
_____
_____

APPLYING YOUR KNOWLEDGE: LEARNING ACTIVITIES

Chapters 8 and 9

1. Research reveals that preschoolers who are exposed to formal lessons are not advanced in motor development. Rather, motor development is influenced by the physical environment in which informal play takes place. Visit several public playgrounds in your community, and describe the play spaces and equipment. Evaluate the extent to which these environments are likely to stimulate young children's running, climbing, jumping, and throwing. Would you make any improvements? Why or why not?

_____

_____

_____

_____

_____

_____

2. Administer either the conservation-of-liquid or the conservation-of-mass (play dough) task illustrated in the Observation Program to two children—one 4 to 5 years old, the other 6 to 8 years old. Be sure to ask each child for a justification of his or her responses: "How come you think so?" or "Can you explain that to me?" For the younger child, after giving the task in the usual way, try relating it to the child's everyday experiences. How does the performance of the younger child differ from that of the older child? Did the younger child's performance improve when you made the task relevant to daily life? (To review these tasks, see Chapter 9, pages 325–326.)

4- to 5-year-old: _____

_____

_____

_____

_____

6- to 8-year-old: _____

_____

_____

_____

_____

Applying Your Knowledge: Learning Activities (continued)

3. Contact a child-care center and ask to observe a group of 2- or 3-year-olds during free play for a 30-minute period. How much time do children spend in make-believe play? Do adults in the center often join in children's make-believe, scaffolding it to a more advanced level? Describe instances in which children engage in pretending (a) by themselves, (b) with peers, and (c) with adults. How do make-believe episodes change in duration and complexity across these contexts?

_____

_____

_____

_____

_____

_____

_____

_____

_____

_____

4. During your visit to a child-care center (described above), watch children as they work on a puzzle, complete an art project, or engage in an activity that requires sustained attention. Are there individual differences in level of sustained attention? Do you notice children using private speech? Describe your observations. _____

_____

_____

_____

_____

_____

_____

_____

5. Using stickers or pictures from magazines, prepare the materials needed for the memory game illustrated in the Observation Program and try it with a 4- to 6-year-old child. Note how many pictures the child recalls. Then embed the need to remember in a meaningful context. For example, ask the child to play shopkeeper, and indicate that it is important to recall all the items for sale in the store. Did the child's memory improve in the second activity? Did he or she use any strategies to aid recall? Explain. _____

_____

_____

_____

_____

_____

_____

Applying Your Knowledge: Learning Activities (continued)

6. Observe a child between 2 and 5 years of age for a 30-minute period, and record all of the child's utterances. Examine the language sample for each of the following features:

A. Number of different words spoken: _____

B. Percentage of words that are object words: _____; action words: _____; state (or modifier) words: _____.

C. Examples of overextensions: _____
_____
_____

D. Average length of sentences (in number of words): _____
_____

E. Examples of complex grammatical constructions: _____
_____
_____
_____

Compare your findings with those of several of your classmates who observed a child of a different age. What do your comparisons reveal about language progress in early childhood?

_____
_____
_____
_____
_____
_____
_____
_____
_____
_____
_____
_____
_____

CHAPTER 10
EMOTIONAL AND SOCIAL DEVELOPMENT
IN EARLY CHILDHOOD

SUMMARY

This section of the Observation Program begins with an overview of the development of peer sociability. As young children interact with peers, gender typing is clearly evident. The contribution of children's play styles to gender segregation is discussed. Development of gender constancy is illustrated by 5-year-old Janaisa's and 7-year-old Zoe's beliefs about whether changing a doll's clothing would result in a change in sex.

Next, the Observation Program illustrates how child-rearing practices influence children's ability to get along in the wider world of peers and preschool, with an emphasis on the impact of child temperament and parenting strategies on early moral internalization.

The diversity of family lifestyles is captured through four interviews: (1) Joanna, a young mother who gave birth to two sons out of wedlock; (2) Bill, the custodial parent of 4-year-old Jeremy, who has cerebral palsy, and 5-year-old Dylan; (3) Jane, a single mother of 3-year-old Emily, adopted from the People's Republic of China; and (4) Deb and Ron, dual-earner parents, who discuss the challenges and rewards of combining careers with parenthood.

Finally, the director of Illinois State University's child-care center discusses the ingredients of high-quality child care.

MASTERING COURSE CONTENT

PEER RELATIONS AND GENDER TYPING

1. As you observe examples of peer interaction in the video, highlight the major advances in peer sociability during the preschool years. Are instances of social problem solving evident in this segment? Explain. (374–375)

A. _____

_____

_____

B. _____

_____

_____

Mastering Course Content (continued)

2. Explain how parents influence early peer relations. (378–379)

_____
_____
_____
_____

3. Gender-stereotyped play and toy choices increase over the preschool years. Explain how the rigidity of young children's gender typing is a joint product of cognitive immaturity and environmental influences. (391–394) _____

_____
_____
_____
_____

4. Both the narrator and your text point out that gender typing is especially strong for boys. Explain why. (391–392) _____

_____
_____
_____
_____

5. As the Observation Program illustrates, boys tend to play more actively and roughly than girls, who prefer quieter activities. According to research in your text, what accounts for this consistent sex difference in play styles? (392) _____

_____
_____
_____
_____

6. How do boys' and girls' play-style preferences join with environmental influences and cognitive factors to promote gender segregation? (392–395) _____

_____
_____
_____
_____

7. According to your text and the Observation Program, how do adults foster compliance and dependency in girls and assertiveness, leadership, and self-reliance in boys? (394)

_____
_____
_____
_____

Mastering Course Content (continued)

8. Record 5-year-old Janaisa's and 7-year-old Zoe's responses to the *gender constancy* task. Does their performance fit with research findings in the text? Explain. (396)

A. _____

_____

_____

B. _____

_____

_____

CHILD REARING

9. Explain why Zacharie's temperament poses a challenge to Joanna in her efforts to use warm, appropriately demanding child rearing. (399–400)

_____

_____

_____

_____

_____

_____

10. The narrator points out that to induce compliance and internalization of moral rules, parents of children like Zacharie must be firm but kind. Which style of child rearing combines these two characteristics? (399) _____

_____

11. Joanna, a single parent, has two sons. Compared to girls, do you think boys are easier or more difficult for single mothers to rear? Explain your answer. (*Hint:* Review sex differences in children's activity levels and play styles on page 391 of the text.)

_____

_____

_____

_____

12. Although more fathers are being granted custody after parental divorce, the arrangement is still uncommon. Why did Bill take custody of Dylan and Jeremy? How did parenthood—especially caring for a son with severe disabilities—change Bill?

A. _____

_____

_____

B. _____

_____

_____

Mastering Course Content (continued)

13. Jane, also a single parent, adopted her daughter Emily in the People's Republic of China. What special child-rearing challenges do adoptive parents often face? (For help in answering this question, review the section on adoption in Chapter 2, pages 65, 67–68)

_____

_____

_____

_____

14. Although Emily spent her first 18 months in unstimulating surroundings and was malnourished, she has developed favorably. In addition to an enriched home environment and good nutrition, what aspects of Jane's parenting, visible in the Observation Program, probably helped Emily develop into a healthy, well-adjusted child? (399–400)

_____

_____

_____

_____

_____

15. What factors beyond the family make combining work and parenthood difficult for Deb and Ron? (514–515) _____

_____

_____

16. Why is work–family role conflict greater for women than for men in dual-earner marriages? What steps have Deb and Ron taken to ease this conflict? (Review the text discussion of Maternal Employment and Dual-Earner Families in Chapter 13, pages 514-515)
A. _____

_____

B. _____

_____

17. The narrator comments, "To employed parents, high-quality child care is vital for protecting their children's development." Describe research findings on the developmental consequences of both high-quality and poor-quality child care. (232–233, 354) _____

_____

_____

_____

_____

Mastering Course Content (continued)

18. The director of Illinois State University's child-care center discusses the ingredients of high-quality child care. List factors she mentions, and compare them to the signs of high-quality child care for preschool children listed on page 354 in Chapter 9. For each factor, indicate whether the child-care center meets or exceeds the standards recommended in your text. _____

_____

_____

_____

_____

_____

_____

BUILDING CONNECTIONS

Chapter 10

1. What gender stereotypes are children likely to learn from the media? Do you think television significantly influences young children's gender stereotyping? Explain. (388–390)

A. _____

_____

_____

B. _____

_____

_____

2. In the segments on cognitive development in early childhood, 4-year-old Zacharie demonstrates that he is a one-dimensional classifier: He can sort a collection of objects differing in color, shape, and size in only one way. In the segments on gender typing, Zacharie shows a clear preference for masculine-stereotyped toys. When Professor Berk offers him a doll, he rejects it. How might Zacharie's cognitive rigidity have contributed to his behavior toward the doll? _____

_____

_____

_____

_____

_____

_____

3. Bill is a divorced custodial parent of two sons. Although Joanna is not divorced, her single-parent status means she faces challenges similar to Bill's. Look ahead to Chapter 13, pages 509–510. Cite two important factors that contribute to children's positive adjustment under these circumstances.

A. _____

_____

B. _____

_____

To what extent are both Bill and Joanna making a concerted effort to ensure that their sons benefit from these factors?_____

_____

_____

Building Connections (continued)

4. Off-camera, Jane mentioned to Professor Berk that the caretakers in the Chinese orphanage where Emily spent her first 18 months referred to Emily as "little smart" because of her outgoing, persistent personality. How might these personal characteristics have contributed to Emily's resilience? (For help with this question, review findings on resilient children on page 10 in Chapter 1 and research on temperament on pages 260–261 in Chapter 7). In listening to Jane's description, what other factors probably helped Emily spring back from adversity?

A. _____

_____

_____

B. _____

_____

_____

_____

5. Review ecological systems theory on pages 25–27 in Chapter 1. What sources within the macrosystem are vital for ensuring high-quality child care? Why is it critical for policy makers to be involved in strengthening government-mandated licensing standards for child-care programs? (*Hint:* Review Public Policies and Child Development on pages 79–80 in Chapter 2.)

A. _____

_____

_____

_____

B. _____

_____

_____

_____

_____

APPLYING YOUR KNOWLEDGE: LEARNING ACTIVITIES

Chapter 10

1. Many adults hold gender-stereotyped beliefs about what is "appropriate" for boys and girls. Interview the parents of a young child. Find out whether, when their child was an infant, they purchased certain colors of clothing or certain toys on the basis of the child's sex. Ask about parental expectations for the child's behavior. Do the parents have gender-stereotyped expectations? Are they aware of gender stereotypes? Are they consciously trying to avoid them? Why or why not? _____

_____

_____

_____

_____

_____

_____

_____

_____

_____

_____

_____

_____

2. Visit a child-care center or preschool and watch for instances of gender typing in children's behavior—for example, gender segregation and choice of activity environments. Next, note teacher behaviors that may encourage and sustain traditional gender-role behavior or, alternatively, promote gender-role flexibility. (For example, do teachers encourage children to play in a gender-typed fashion? Do they more often assign girls to structured activities, thereby promoting compliance and dependency?) Record your observations and compare them with research presented in Chapter 10.

_____

_____

_____

_____

_____

_____

_____

_____

_____

_____

_____

_____

_____

_____

Applying Your Knowledge: Learning Activities (continued)

3. Watch television for a half-hour period at three different times of the day when young children are likely to view (early morning, late afternoon, and early evening). List traditional gender-role themes evident in the programs you watch. Also document acts of violence in these programs. How do your findings compare with research presented in the text?

Viewing Period 1: Time of Day _____

Program: _____

_____

_____

_____

Viewing Period 2: Time of Day _____

Program: _____

_____

_____

_____

Viewing Period 3: Time of Day _____

Program: _____

_____

_____

_____

4. Imagine that you have been asked to speak to a group of parents about appropriate forms of discipline for young children. Be sure to explain the styles of child rearing in terms that parents will be able to understand. Also make sure that your presentation includes examples and research that support your comments. _____

_____

_____

_____

_____

_____

_____

_____

_____

_____

_____

_____

_____

CHAPTERS 11–13

MIDDLE CHILDHOOD

PARTICIPANTS

Child	Age	To identify on DVD, look for …
Claire	5 years	White bow in hair, pink dress
Shawn	5 years	Blue striped shirt
Justin	6 years	Green shirt
Liesl	7 years	Long dark hair, white and flowered shirt
Victor	7 years	White, short-sleeved T-shirt
Zoe	7 years	Light blue T-shirt
Lisa	15 years	Olive green shirt

• Elementary school children, parents, and teachers of Thomas Metcalf Laboratory School, Illinois State University
• Elementary school children, parents, and teachers of Keeping Ourselves Safe, New Zealand's national child abuse prevention program
• Owen Sanders, National Director, Keeping Ourselves Safe, New Zealand
• Teachers and children at Swallowcliffe School, suburban South Australia, primary classrooms

CHAPTERS 11 AND 12
PHYSICAL AND COGNITIVE DEVELOPMENT IN MIDDLE CHILDHOOD

SUMMARY

This section opens with body growth in middle childhood. Excerpts from a physical education class at Metcalf School depict physical changes and their implications for motor accomplishments. Later, the Children's Circus at Metcalf School illustrates training of bodily/kinesthetic abilities.

The Observation Program then turns to cognitive development by highlighting the logical reasoning of Piaget's concrete operational stage through children's performance on conservation and class inclusion tasks. Zoe's comments about how to do well on a memory task reveal the development of memory strategies and metacognition in middle childhood. Applications of information processing to literacy and mathematical development are shown through visits to Metcalf School classrooms.

Howard Gardner's theory of multiple intelligences underscores the diversity of human mental abilities, not all of which are represented on current tests. A fourth-grade class in which many learning activities are organized around Gardner's multiple intelligences is shown. The Children's Circus at Metcalf School provides a context for discussing the many factors that contribute to development of creativity and special talents.

Next, the Observation Program visits several primary classrooms at Swallowcliffe School in Australia. A new administration has transformed the school from a run-down, neglected state into a unique place where cooperative learning takes place at all levels.

MASTERING COURSE CONTENT

BODY GROWTH AND MOTOR DEVELOPMENT

Chapter 11

1. How do both heredity and environment contribute to differences in body size? What differences are evident in the Observation Program? (413)

A. _____

_____

B. _____

_____

2. Describe physical changes in middle childhood that lead to improvements in flexibility, balance, agility, and strength. Include examples from the Observation Program in your answer. (427–428) _____

_____

_____

_____

_____

_____

_____

_____

3. Using examples to support your answer, explain how the Children's Circus appeals to and supports individual differences in motor capacities. Are sex differences in athletic ability evident? (428–430)

A. _____

_____

_____

B. _____

_____

_____

Mastering Course Content (continued)

4. Second through eighth graders participate in the Children's Circus at Metcalf School, practicing several times a week. Many work on athletic and entertainment skills for five to seven years. How does the Children's Circus promote physical activity and health in all participants? Do you think participating in the Children's Circus is an effective way to combat childhood obesity? Explain. (416–419)

A. _____
_____
_____

B. _____
_____
_____

COGNITIVE DEVELOPMENT

Chapter 12

Piaget's Concrete Operational Stage

5. Cite two characteristics of *concrete operational* reasoning illustrated by 7-year-old Victor's response to the conservation-of-mass problem, and indicate how Victor's explanation portrays each characteristic. (438)

A. _____
_____

B. _____
_____

6. When given a class inclusion task, what does 7-year-old Victor say that indicates he grasps the idea of hierarchical classification? (438) _____
_____
_____
_____

7. Explain how culture and schooling contribute to the mastery of Piagetian tasks. (440)
_____
_____
_____

Mastering Course Content (continued)

Information Processing

8. How do information-processing theorists explain the development of logical thinking? (440–441) _____
_____
_____
_____

9. How might an information-processing theorist explain the differences between 4-year-old Alison's and 7-year-old Victor's approach to Piaget's conservation tasks? (If you need to review the footage of Alison, return to the Early Childhood section of the Observation Program.) (440–441) _____
_____
_____
_____
_____
_____

10. Cite three ways that attention changes during middle childhood. (443–444)
A. _____
_____
B. _____
_____
C. _____
_____

11. Zoe's performance on a task requiring retention of discrete bits of information differs sharply from that of people in non-Western cultures who have no formal schooling. Why does deliberate use of memory strategies accompany formal schooling? (446–447)
_____
_____
_____
_____

12. Zoe has substantial *metacognitive knowledge* about how to remember. Describe what she knows, and explain why metacognition is likely to help Zoe when she faces a recall task. (447–448)
_____
_____
_____
_____

Mastering Course Content (continued)

13. What do Zoe's responses to Professor Berk reveal about her understanding of false belief? Why is mastery of false belief a landmark achievement? (447)

A. _____

_____

B. _____

_____

14. List factors that may have contributed to Zoe's mastery of false belief. (447–448)

_____

_____

_____

15. As you observe students' activities at Metcalf School, describe aspects of information processing being applied to literacy and mathematical instruction. (449–452)

_____

_____

_____

_____

Intelligence

16. Briefly describe the controversy surrounding the use of IQ tests in educational decisions. What is your opinion on the matter, and why? (452–454)

A. _____

_____

_____

_____

B. _____

_____

_____

_____

17. Summarize *Sternberg's triarchic theory of successful intelligence*. How does Sternberg's theory differ from traditional intelligence theories? (454–455)

A. _____

_____

B. _____

_____

_____

Mastering Course Content (continued)

18. Which of the following of *Gardner's multiple intelligences* are represented on currently available tests for children? Which are not represented? (455–456)

_____ Yes/No Linguistic   _____ Yes/No Bodily/Kinesthetic
_____ Yes/No Logico-mathematical   _____ Yes/No Naturalist
_____ Yes/No Musical   _____ Yes/No Interpersonal
_____ Yes/No Spatial   _____ Yes/No Intrapersonal

19. Review the visit to the fourth-grade class, in which many learning activities are organized around Gardner's theory of multiple intelligences. Children take on different roles from one assignment to the next, with the goal of fostering many mental abilities. In an assignment in which children use clues to figure out the meaning of novel symbols, indicate which intelligences are promoted by each of the following roles: (455–456)
Recorder: _____
_____

Problem solver: _____
_____

Encourager: _____
_____

20. The narrator points out that in addition to bodily/kinesthetic intelligence, the Children's Circus fosters interpersonal intelligence. Cite examples that support this statement. (456) _____
_____
_____
_____

Children's Learning in School

21. Explain how schools foster cognitive development during middle childhood. (467–470) ____
_____
_____
_____
_____

22. According to the Observation Program and your text, what are some benefits of multigrade grouping? (470) _____
_____
_____
_____
_____

Mastering Course Content (continued)

23. Swallowcliffe School encourages cooperative learning in children as young as 5 years of age. Summarize the cognitive and social benefits of cooperative learning. (470)

_____

_____

_____

_____

24. Swallowcliffe School makes a concerted effort to involve parents in their children's education. Why does this school believe parent–school involvement is critical to its success? ____

_____

_____

_____

25. Why might the cooperative learning approach at Swallowcliffe School be well-suited to accommodating children with disabilities in regular classrooms? (472)

_____

_____

_____

_____

BUILDING CONNECTIONS

CHAPTERS 11 AND 12

1. Metacognitive knowledge is important not just for cognitive problem solving, but also for social competence. Review the section on social problem solving in Chapter 10, pages 377–378. What do children have to be *aware of* to solve social problems effectively?

_____

_____

_____

_____

_____

2. Your text indicates that although metacognitive knowledge increases with age, school-age children do not always apply what they know about mental activity to improve their performance. What does Vygotsky's theory suggest about how to foster self-regulation? Why is it important to offer children explanations for the effectiveness of self-regulatory strategies? (448–449)

A. _____

_____

_____

B. _____

_____

_____

3. As you observe students at Metcalf School, evaluate the quality of each classroom. You may find the Applying What We Know table on page 466 of your text helpful.

_____

_____

_____

_____

_____

_____

Building Connections (continued)

4. Piaget's theory has inspired research into many aspects of children's development. Select two of the following: self-concept (Chapter 13, pages 482–483); perspective taking (Chapter 13, pages 491–492); moral reasoning (Chapter 13, pages 491–492); friendship (Chapter 13, page 499). Explain how changes from early to middle childhood reflect cognitive advances, as described by Piaget.

A. _____

_____

_____

_____

_____

B. _____

_____

_____

_____

_____

5. At Swallowcliffe School, teachers show children how to collaborate. What Vygotskian concepts are consistent with this approach? Explain. (See Chapter 9, pages 333–336.)

_____

_____

_____

_____

_____

6. At Swallowcliffe School, older children tutor and support younger children. What are the benefits of peer tutoring for both the tutors and tutees? Explain how such benefits probably arise in the peer tutoring context. Why is it important for adult teachers to train and supervise peer tutors? Do you think such training takes place at Swallowcliffe School? Why or why not? (470, 472)

A. _____

_____

B. _____

_____

C. _____

_____

D. _____

_____

Building Connections (continued)

7. As you read about class size, educational philosophies, teacher-student interaction, and grouping practices, reflect on your own school experiences. How would you rate the quality of your elementary school experiences? (467–470)

_____

_____

_____

_____

APPLYING YOUR KNOWLEDGE: LEARNING ACTIVITIES

Chapters 11 and 12

1. The text indicates that *secular trends in physical growth*—changes in body size and rate of growth from one generation to the next—have occurred in industrialized nations (see page 413). Record adult height and the approximate age at which it was attained for yourself, your same-sex parent, and a same-sex grandparent. (If you cannot obtain this information from your own family members, ask a friend to provide it for his or her family.) To what extent are your findings consistent with the existence of a secular trend? What factors probably account for secular trends in physical growth?

_____
_____
_____
_____
_____
_____
_____
_____
_____
_____
_____
_____
_____
_____

2. Interview a 5- to 6-year-old and a 7- to 9-year-old for knowledge of memory strategies, using the following questions as well as one or two that you make up yourself:

A. When you try to remember things, do you remember some things better than others? What kinds of things are hard to remember? Which ones are easier to remember? _____
_____
_____
_____

B. Suppose I wanted you to remember some pictures. I give you three minutes to look at them, and then I take them away. What would you do to learn the pictures? _____
_____
_____
_____

C. Suppose I tell you a story and ask you to remember it. Would it be easier to remember it word for word or in your own words? Why? _____
_____
_____
_____
_____

Applying Your Knowledge: Learning Activities (continued)

Describe each child's responses:

5- to 6-year-old: _____
_____
_____
_____
_____
_____

7- to 9-year-old: _____
_____
_____
_____
_____
_____

Did metacognitive knowledge increase with age? What factors—both internal to the child and in the child's experiences—probably contribute to the development of metacognition during this age period? _____
_____
_____
_____
_____
_____
_____

3. Arrange to observe several periods of academic instruction in an elementary school classroom. Cite examples of how the teacher promotes each of the following aspects of information processing:

Use of memory strategies: _____
_____
_____
_____
_____

Metacognitive knowledge: _____
_____
_____
_____

Cognitive self-regulation: _____
_____
_____
_____

Building Connections (continued)

Basic reading and mathematical skills: _____

_____

_____

_____

_____

_____

Reading comprehension and/or appreciation of the uses of mathematics: _____

_____

_____

_____

_____

_____

Scientific reasoning: _____

_____

_____

_____

_____

_____

4. Suppose that children's intelligence is assessed in the following two situations: (a) using a standardized intelligence test in their elementary classroom and (b) on the basis of their performance over time in the Children's Circus. To what extent are the two assessments likely to be correlated? How well is each assessment likely to predict scholastic performance? How about later life success? Explain.

_____

_____

_____

_____

_____

_____

_____

_____

_____

Building Connections (continued)

5. The narrator comments that any child, no matter what his or her native gifts, can participate in the Children's Circus. What characteristics of this learning environment grant low-SES and ethnic minority children the opportunity to excel, in contrast to traditional academic contexts, where they typically fall behind their middle-SES peers?

_____
_____
_____
_____
_____
_____
_____
_____
_____
_____

6. Pose the following question to several friends or family members: How well educated are North American children? Specifically, how does their educational achievement compare to children in other industrialized countries? Record their responses, and show them figure 12.8 on page 475 of your text. Were their responses accurate? If not, were they surprised by the research? Explain.

_____
_____
_____
_____
_____
_____
_____
_____
_____
_____

CHAPTER 13
EMOTIONAL AND SOCIAL DEVELOPMENT
IN MIDDLE CHILDHOOD

SUMMARY

In this section, the Observation Program examines how children's cognition and social experiences expand in middle childhood and adolescence, leading them to think more about themselves. School-age children's self-descriptions reflect the development of self-concept, from concrete characteristics and typical emotions and behaviors to personality traits. Five-year-old Claire and 7-year-old Liesl play a game that reveals gains in perspective taking during the early school years. Children's concepts of friendship are illustrated by their responses to the question, "What makes a good friend?" The importance of social experience—in particular, the guidance of parents and teachers—in children's grasp of interpersonal relations is emphasized.

In middle childhood, great strides also take place in moral understanding. On a distributive justice task, 7-year-old Zoe shows a strong commitment to sharing equally. Finally, the Observation Program visits Keeping Ourselves Safe, a national child abuse prevention program in New Zealand. With the assistance of specially trained police officers, teachers implement the program in the public schools and involve parents, since home and school must work together so that children receive consistent safety messages.

MASTERING COURSE CONTENT

SELF-CONCEPT, PERSPECTIVE TAKING, AND FRIENDSHIP

1. Cite examples from Zoe's and Lisa's self-descriptions depicted in the Observation Program. How do the examples illustrate a major change in self-concept during middle childhood? (482–483)

A. _____

_____

_____

B. _____

_____

_____

2. What major change in children's self-descriptions takes place between 8 and 11 years of age? (482–483) _____

_____

_____

_____

_____

_____

Mastering Course Content (continued)

3. Based on Zoe's self-description from question 1, are her remarks typical of the self-concepts of school-age children? Explain. What changes in self-concept take place from early to middle childhood? (483)

A. _____

_____

B. _____

_____

4. In contrast to 5-year-old Claire, who has a partial understanding, 7-year-old Liesl indicates that neither a child her age nor a baby would be able to identify a picture of a horse from a nondescript part. What does Liesl's reasoning indicate about her perspective-taking skills? (491–492) _____

_____

_____

_____

5. Explain how *perspective taking* is related to social skills. Does Liesl's perspective taking suggest that she will get along well with adults and peers? (491–492)

_____

_____

_____

_____

6. How do gains in perspective taking contribute to moral understanding? (492–493)

_____

_____

_____

7. What is meant by *distributive justice?* Record 7-year-old Zoe's responses to the distributive justice dilemma. At what level of distributive justice is she? (491, 497–501)

A. _____

_____

B. _____

_____

C. _____

_____

8. Victor realizes that an important ingredient of friendship is common values. List attributes on which friends tend to resemble one another. (499) _____

_____

_____

_____

_____

Name _____
Date _____

Mastering Course Content (continued)

9. At age 7, Victor is advanced in his grasp of the meaning of friendship. How can classroom learning activities promote social understanding? What does Alyssa's essay reveal about her conception of friendship? (499)

A. _____

_____

B. _____

_____

10. How might gender-stereotyped beliefs influence friendship and peer relations in middle childhood? (503–504) _____

_____

_____

_____

CHILD ABUSE PREVENTION

11. Keeping Ourselves Safe, New Zealand's national child abuse prevention program, teaches children that when abuse occurs, it is often someone close to them, not a stranger, who is responsible. Why is this type of information important? (517)

_____

_____

_____

12. According to Freda Briggs, why is parent involvement vital to the success of Keeping Ourselves Safe? (*Hint:* Think back to ecological systems theory, described in Chapter 1, especially the importance of the mesosystem.) _____

_____

_____

_____

13. When it began, what impact did Keeping Ourselves Safe have on child abuse reports in New Zealand? _____

_____

_____

_____

Mastering Course Content (continued)

14. Freda Briggs notes that beginning in preschool, parents should start labeling body parts with correct terminology rather than using "pet names." According to Dr. Briggs, why is this important, and how does labeling body parts help protect children from sexual abuse?

A. _____

_____

B. _____

_____

15. Keeping Ourselves Safe is a unique program, since no other country in the world has a national strategy for preventing child sexual abuse. Why do you think national efforts of this kind are so rare? _____

_____

_____

_____

_____

_____

BUILDING CONNECTIONS

Chapter 13

1. Piaget's theory has inspired research on many aspects of development. Explain how changes in self-concept from middle childhood to adolescence reflect cognitive advances, as described by Piaget. (For help, review Piaget's Theory, pages 437–442.)

_____
_____
_____
_____
_____
_____
_____

2. Perspective taking is vital for many aspects of social understanding. Return to Chapter 10, page 373, and review the section on empathy. Explain how advances in perspective taking contribute to the development of empathy. _____

_____
_____
_____
_____
_____
_____
_____
_____
_____
_____

3. Review the four styles of child rearing discussed on pages 399–400 of your text. How might each style of parenting contribute to the school-age child's reasoning about distributive justice, moral rules, social conventions, and matters of personal choice? (492–493) _____

_____
_____
_____
_____
_____
_____
_____
_____

Building Connections (continued)

4. Review school-age children's self-descriptions and their comments about what it means to be a good friend in the Observation Program. Notice that children seem to be more advanced in friendship understanding than in self-concept. Recall from Chapters 9 and 12 that children's cognitive development is often uneven across tasks. Why might these children's ideas about friendship be more mature than their self-perceptions?

_____

_____

_____

_____

_____

_____

_____

_____

_____

_____

5. Owen Sanders, national director of Keeping Ourselves Safe, points out that the program cannot simply be transplanted from one country to another. Each community and nation must design and develop its own child abuse prevention strategies to meet its unique needs. From what you have learned about cultural variations in attitudes and values, why is Sanders's advice valid? Do you think a program like Keeping Ourselves Safe would be accepted broadly in your community and culture? Why or why not?

A. _____

_____

_____

B. _____

_____

_____

APPLYING YOUR KNOWLEDGE: LEARNING ACTIVITIES

Chapter 13

1. Interview two children—a preschooler and a school-age child—to explore their self-concepts. Begin by asking a general question—for example, "Tell me about yourself." Then follow up with more specific queries addressing children's likes and dislikes and beliefs about their own competencies—for example, "What do you think you are good at and not good at?" Take notes on the children's responses. What did each emphasize: name, physical appearance, everyday emotions and behaviors, or personality traits? How do their answers compare with research in the text?

Preschool-age child: _____

_____

_____

_____

School-age child: _____

_____

_____

_____

_____

Comparison: _____

_____

_____

_____

2. Interview three children—a preschooler, a school-age child, and an adolescent—to explore their concept of friendship. Use questions like "What does it mean to be a good friend?" or "Why is it nice to have a friend?" Note each child's responses. Do concepts of friendship reflect the age-related changes described in your text? Explain, citing examples from your interviews.

Preschool-age child: _____

_____

_____

School-age child: _____

_____

_____

Adolescent: _____

_____

_____

Comparison with text: _____

_____

_____

Applying Your Knowledge: Learning Activities (continued)

3. Arrange to observe for a one- to two-hour period in an elementary, middle or junior high school, or high school classroom. Indicate whether or not you observed each of the following characteristics, which support academic and social learning. For each characteristic, describe precisely what you saw.

Small class size: _____
_____
_____

Challenging learning activities: _____
_____
_____

Learning activities that involve communication and collaboration: _____
_____
_____

Teachers who promote high-level thinking: _____
_____
_____

Teachers who are responsive and encouraging: _____
_____
_____

CHAPTERS 14–16

ADOLESCENCE

PARTICIPANTS

• Joel, age 18, Rhiannon, age 18, and Jacob, their 1-year-old son
• Ray and Laurie, Joel's parents
• High school students in social studies and math classes, University High School, Illinois State University
• Eighth-grade discussion group at Thomas Metcalf School, Illinois State University
• Jean, Phil, and Carla, 17-year-old seniors at University High School, Illinois State University
• Best friends, 13-year-old Mari and 14-year-old Sarah
• Mike, 18 years, and Haley, 17 years, high school seniors
• Mark, a 24-year-old college student

CHAPTERS 14 AND 15
PHYSICAL AND COGNITIVE DEVELOPMENT
IN ADOLESCENCE

SUMMARY

This section of the Observation Program opens with the dramatic physical changes of puberty, which lead to an adult-sized body and sexual maturity. When adolescents become sexually active without using contraception, the consequences can be profound, as Rhiannon and Joel's story reveals. After dating Joel for a year, Rhiannon discovered that she was pregnant. Joel and Rhiannon share their reactions to the pregnancy and describe how the arrival of Jacob, their son, has changed their lives. Ray and Laurie relate their concerns about the effect of teenage childbearing on their son's future.

Next, the Observation Program focuses on cognitive development by demonstrating how, during adolescence, young people become better at thinking abstractly. Piaget's formal operational stage is illustrated through visits to high school social studies and math classes, where students engage in hypothetico-deductive reasoning and propositional thought.

MASTERING COURSE CONTENT

PUBERTY

1. True or False: Girls generally become physically and sexually mature about two years earlier than boys. (531) _____

2. At puberty, large sex differences in body size, proportions, and composition appear. After observing adolescents participating in the Children's Circus, describe these physical differences. (531–533) _____

_____

_____

_____

_____

3. What implications do sex differences in physical growth have for the development of motor skills? (533–535) _____

_____

_____

_____

4. Provide two explanations for pubertal timing effects. (541–542)

A. _____

_____

B. _____

_____

5. Describe long-term consequences of variations in pubertal timing, highlighting sex differences. (541–543) _____

_____

_____

_____

Mastering Course Content (continued)

TEENAGE PREGNANCY AND CHILDBEARING

6. Rhiannon and Joel's story is not unique. The United States has the highest rate of adolescent pregnancy and parenthood in the Western industrialized world. What three factors increase the incidence of adolescent pregnancy? (555)

A. _____

_____

B. _____

_____

C. _____

_____

7. The narrator states that teenage parenthood can have profound consequences for three generations. Describe its potential consequences for (a) Joel and Rhiannon; (b) Jacob; and (c) Ray and Laurie. (556–557)

A. _____

_____

B. _____

_____

C. _____

_____

8. Joel and Rhiannon decided not to marry. Nevertheless, both have taken on the responsibilities of parenthood. What is distinctive about Joel's response to adolescent parenthood? (556–557) ___

_____

_____

_____

9. Both Joel and Rhiannon have parents who have supported them and participated in the rearing of Jacob. How does family support contribute to the well-being of adolescent parents and their children? (558–559) _____

_____

_____

_____

COGNITIVE DEVELOPMENT

Chapter 15

PIAGET'S THEORY: THE FORMAL OPERATIONAL STAGE

10. Describe the two main features of Piaget's *formal operational stage* depicted in the high school history and math classes. (566–567)

A. _____

_____

B. _____

_____

11. Describe research that supports the narrator's conclusion that schooling contributes greatly to the development of formal operational thought. (568–569)

_____

_____

_____

_____

_____

12. According to the information-processing view, what factors contribute to adolescent cognitive development? (569)

_____

_____

_____

_____

13. The text discusses how metacognitive knowledge contributes to the development of scientific reasoning. Briefly summarize this research, and suggest ways that teachers can promote scientific reasoning. (569–571)

A. _____

_____

_____

B. _____

_____

_____

_____

Mastering Course Content (continued)

LEARNING IN SCHOOL

14. Explain how the activities taking place in the social studies and math classes support high achievement. (580–581) _____

_____

_____

_____

_____

15. In addition to schools, what other factors support academic achievement in adolescence? (580–581) _____

_____

_____

_____

_____

CHAPTER 16
EMOTIONAL AND SOCIAL DEVELOPMENT IN ADOLESCENCE

SUMMARY

During adolescence, peer groups become important contexts for social learning. The impact of puberty and perspective taking on gender-role development in early adolescence is considered as eighth graders talk about their own and their peers' capacities and behaviors. For both adolescent boys and girls, friendship plays an important role in the development of self-esteem and identity. Mari and Sarah, best friends, talk about the meaning and importance of friendship. Then, 17-year-old Haley and 18-year-old Mike describe their dating relationship.

As adolescents' cognitive and social experiences expand, they think more about themselves. Teenagers combine their various personality traits into an organized self-concept, which provides a foundation for identity development. Jean, Phil, and Carla, University High School students, discuss their experiences in constructing an identity. Mark, a college student, looks back on his struggle to formulate a sexual identity in adolescence.

MASTERING COURSE CONTENT

SELF-CONCEPT, PERSPECTIVE TAKING, AND IDENTITY DEVELOPMENT

1. Cite qualities that Jean emphasizes in her self-description. How do these qualities differ from the way school-age children describe themselves? (599)

A. _____

_____

_____

B. _____

_____

_____

2. How do adolescents' self-descriptions provide the foundation for identity development? (599–600) _____

_____

_____

_____

Mastering Course Content (continued)

3. Describe how parents and teachers influence adolescents' self-esteem. (600–601)

_____

_____

_____

4. Phil explains that he is much less concerned about how others view him as a senior than he was when he entered high school. What factors probably contribute to this change? (603–604) __

_____

_____

_____

5. Describe factors that made it difficult for Mark to formulate a positive homosexual identity. Then describe conditions that encouraged Mark to "come out"—that is, to be forthright with himself and others about his homosexuality.(602–604)

A. _____

_____

B. _____

_____

6. Carla describes some conflict with her parents as she defines her own values. Using research from the text to support your answer, explain how Carla's parents can help foster her identity development. (603) _____

_____

_____

_____

_____

GENDER TYPING

7. Cite biological, cognitive, and social influences on the rise in gender typing in early adolescence. (615)

Biological: _____

_____

Cognitive: _____

_____

Social: _____

_____

Mastering Course Content (continued)

8. How does the eighth graders' discussion illustrate *gender intensification* in early adolescence? (615) _____

_____

_____

_____

_____

9. How does the eighth graders' discussion illustrate the finding that gender-stereotyped beliefs vary greatly from child to child? (615) _____

_____

_____

_____

PEER RELATIONS

10. Describe similarities between Mari and Sarah's discussion of friendship and research presented in the text. (620–621) _____

_____

_____

_____

_____

11. How do Mari and Sarah explain sex differences in friendships? According to your text, why do these differences exist? (Chapter 16, pp. 621–622)

A. _____

_____

_____

B. _____

_____

_____

12. In the video, Sarah and Mari explain that friendships tend to form between individuals with similar cultural backgrounds. Yet, although Mari and Sarah have different cultural backgrounds, they are best friends. What factors have allowed their friendship to blossom? (621–622) _____

_____

_____

_____

_____

Mastering Course Content (continued)

13. Research indicates that childhood and adolescent friendships are related to many aspects of psychological health and competence into early adulthood. Explain why. (622)

_____

_____

_____

_____

14. Cite some benefits of adolescent dating. How do dating experiences in adolescence influence romantic relationships in adulthood? (624–625)

A. _____

_____

_____

B. _____

_____

_____

15. Describe qualities that Mike and Haley were initially drawn to in one another. How is their relationship different from the dating experiences of younger adolescents? (624–625)

A. _____

_____

B. _____

_____

_____

16. Based on their discussion, do you think Mike and Haley's relationship will continue as they make the transition to college? Why or why not? (624–625)

_____

_____

_____

_____

BUILDING CONNECTIONS

Chapters 14-16

1. Early adolescence is a time of increased gender stereotyping of interests, attitudes, and behavior. How might the arrival of puberty contribute to this trend? (531–533)

_____

_____

_____

_____

_____

_____

_____

2. Review ecological systems theory on pages 27-29 of your text. How have interactions between various levels of the environment contributed to favorable outcomes for Joel, Rhiannon, and Jacob? _____

_____

_____

_____

_____

_____

3. Cognitive processes are important in identity development. Explain how critical and abstract thinking are involved in adolescent identity formation. List environmental factors that contribute to adolescent identity formation. (573, 601–604)

A. _____

_____

B. _____

_____

_____

4. Describe common challenges faced by homosexual and ethnic-minority youths in forging a positive sense of identity. What environmental supports can help both homosexual and ethnic minority adolescents develop a healthy identity? (Chapter 14, pages 552–553; Chapter 16, page 605)

A. _____

_____

_____

B. _____

_____

_____

Building Connections (continued)

5. Review the benefits of adolescent friendship. Explain why the close friendship between Mari and Sarah is likely to ease both girls' transition from junior high to high school. (622) _____

_____

_____

_____

_____

_____

APPLYING YOUR KNOWLEDGE: LEARNING ACTIVITIES

Chapters 14–16

1. Are you or any of your friends personally acquainted with someone who became an adolescent parent? Did he or she graduate from high school? Enroll in college? How well are the parent and child faring now? What factors do you suspect contributed to favorable or unfavorable outcomes, and how well do those factors compare with research in your text? (Chapter 15, pages 555–556) _

_____
_____
_____
_____
_____
_____
_____
_____
_____
_____
_____

2. Supportive home and school environments can enhance identity development in adolescence. Select one of the following activities:

A. Provide advice to parents who want to nurture their teenager's identity development. In addition, indicate which parenting practices are associated with a foreclosed or diffused identity status. Reflecting on your own adolescence, in which ways did your parents foster or hinder your identity development? _____

_____
_____
_____
_____

B. Provide advice to high school personnel for nurturing students' identity development. What teaching practices, school services, and activities would be helpful? Reflecting on your own adolescence, in what ways did your high school experience foster or hinder your identity development? _____

_____
_____
_____
_____
_____
_____

Applying Your Knowledge: Learning Activities (continued)

3. Identify a friend or acquaintance who is a member of a minority group, and ask permission to interview him or her about personal experiences in forging an ethnic identity. What challenges did this individual face, and how did he or she attempt to resolve them? _____

_____

_____

_____

_____

_____

_____

_____

_____

_____

_____

CHAPTER 17

EMERGING ADULTHOOD

PARTICIPANTS

- Casey, 22 years
- Elizabeth, 24 years, and Joel, 25 years

SUMMARY

As this section of the Observation Program opens, 25-year-old Casey is discussing her identity and her dreams for the future. Like many young people her age, Casey is in a period of development referred to as *emerging adulthood.* She has left adolescence but has not yet fully assumed adult responsibilities. Next, 24-year-old Elizabeth and 25-year-old Joel discuss the transition to adulthood, including how they will know when they reach this milestone.

MASTERING COURSE CONTENT

DEVELOPMENT IN EMERGING ADULTHOOD

1. What role has culture played in the extended transition from adolescence to adulthood? (643–644) _____

_____

_____

2. Cite cognitive, emotional, and social changes that accompany development in *emerging adulthood.* (645–649)

Cognitive: _____

_____

Emotional: _____

_____

Social: _____

_____

Mastering Course Content (continued)

3. What are some benefits of a prolonged transition from adolescence to adulthood? Is there any downside? Explain, using examples from the Observation Program and research presented in your text. (642–652)

A. _____

_____

B. _____

_____

4. What factors have contributed to Casey's identity development? Are these factors consistent with research presented in the text? Why or why not? (645–647)

_____

_____

_____

_____

5. What dreams does Casey mention? Are her dreams consistent with those of many career-oriented women? Explain. (649–650)

A. _____

_____

B. _____

_____

6. While Casey is a successful college student with plans to continue her education, ethnic minority students have an increased risk for dropping out of college. What challenges do ethnic minorities face in emerging adulthood? (650–651)

_____

_____

_____

_____

7. Explain why women often experience obstacles to success as they enter college and the workforce. What factors can help them overcome these obstacles? (649–650)

A. _____

_____

B. _____

_____

Mastering Course Content (continued)

8. What makes emerging adulthood a particularly stressful time of life? What factors can help Casey, Elizabeth, and Joel overcome these stressors? (652–654)

A. _____

_____

_____

B. _____

_____

_____

9. According to Erikson (Chapter 1, pages 14–16), intimacy is a major task of early adulthood. What emphasis do Elizabeth and Joel place on intimacy and romantic relationships? Is this consistent with research presented in your text? Explain. (Chapter 17, pp. 647–648)

A. _____

_____

B. _____

_____

BUILDING CONNECTIONS

Chapter 17

1. How might identity development in adolescence influence the transition to adulthood? (Chapter 16, pp. 602–604) _____

_____

_____

_____

_____

2. Describe cognitive differences between adolescents and emerging adults. What experiences likely contribute to these differences? (645–646)

A. _____

_____

B. _____

_____

_____

3. Return to Chapter 1 (page 10) and review research on resilient children. How do factors that protect children from stressful events also protect young people as they transition from adolescence to adulthood? _____

_____

_____

_____

_____

4. How might access to meaningful work activities during adolescence help emerging adults find fulfilling vocations? (649–650) _____

_____

_____

_____

_____

APPLYING YOUR KNOWLEDGE: LEARNING ACTIVITIES

Chapter 17

1. Pose the following question to several of your friends or classmates: *Do you consider yourself to have fully reached adulthood? Your options for answering are "yes," "no," or "yes and no."* Next, ask them to explain their responses. Based on the information you gathered, are these individuals in the stage of emerging adulthood or have they fully reached adulthood? Explain.

_____
_____
_____
_____
_____
_____
_____
_____
_____
_____
_____
_____
_____

2. Now that you have read Chapter 17 and observed young people describing characteristics of emerging adulthood, would you say that you are currently in this period of development? Why or why not? If you feel you have officially entered adulthood, how did you know when you reached this milestone? If you believe you have not yet reached adulthood, how will you know when you have made the transition?

_____
_____
_____
_____
_____
_____
_____
_____
_____
_____
_____
_____
_____
_____

Applying Your Knowledge: Learning Activities (continued)

3. Interview two people, one between ages 40 and 60 and one older than age 60. Ask both to describe their experiences as they made the transition from adolescence to adulthood. Note differences between the generations. What does each person recall about his or her educational and vocational opportunities? When did each know he or she had become an adult? Do their experiences differ from those presented in the text? Explain.

_____
_____
_____
_____
_____
_____
_____
_____
_____
_____
_____
_____
_____
_____

SUGGESTIONS FOR OBSERVING AND INTERVIEWING YOUNG CHILDREN

Below are some suggestions for observing and interviewing young children that will help you avoid common difficulties encountered by individuals new to these experiences.

ASKING PERMISSION

Explain to the child's parent, guardian, or teacher what you want to do and why you want to do it. Then ask permission to observe or interview. For children 3 years and older, provide the child with an age-appropriate explanation and ask if he or she would like to participate. For example, you might say to a young child, "I want to know how children your age play these games and how they answer some questions. Would you like to help me?"

Ask permission, even if you are observing in a public place. Parents (and some children) are likely to become uncomfortable when they see you watching and do not know the purpose of your activities.

OBSERVING

Observer Influence

Making observations always entails the risk of *observer influence*—the possibility that because of your presence, children and adults will behave in unnatural ways. To handle this problem, become acquainted with those you wish to observe, and build an image of a friendly, nonevaluating individual by explaining what you are doing to parents and teachers—and to children who are old enough to understand.

Before beginning, spend some time in the setting so children become accustomed to your presence. Most infants and preschoolers readily get used to being observed; they cannot stop being themselves for very long. For older children, a longer adaptation period may be necessary.

You can, to some extent, check whether your presence affected children's behavior. After you have observed, ask the parent or teacher whether the child's activity differed from what is typical.

Recording Observations

Review the procedures for observing children in Chapter 1 of the text. If your goal is to collect a broad range of information, use the specimen record, a description of everything said and done over a certain time period. Even better, whisper a description of the child's activities into a tape recorder, and transcribe your remarks as soon as possible.

Suggestions for Observing and Interviewing Young Children (continued)

If you are interested in only one or a few behaviors, *event sampling*—a description of all instances of a particular behavior during a specified time period—is a more efficient procedure. Alternatively, you can use *time sampling* by preparing a checklist of the behaviors of interest and indicating whether each occurred during a series of brief time periods. For example, you might watch the child for 15 seconds and check off behaviors during the next 15 seconds, repeating this process until the observation period is complete.

INTERVIEWING

Rapport Building

Insofar as possible, sit so you are facing the child. Begin by establishing rapport; for example, ask the child about his or her interests and recent experiences. If the child is reluctant to talk, play a game that requires little or no verbal interaction, such as throwing and catching a ball. This gives the child a chance to feel comfortable with you.

Orienting Materials

Make sure you orient materials toward the child rather than yourself. A line of chips in conservation of number or a set of straws of different lengths in seriation looks quite different to a young child when viewed from the side rather than head-on. If you are not careful about orienting materials, you may not get responses that represent the child's thinking.

Phrasing Questions Clearly

Phrase your questions specifically enough to the child so there is little opportunity for ambiguity. For example, when giving conservation tasks, do not merely say, "Are these the same?" (too vague). Refer to the dimension of the task you have in mind: "Is there the same amount of (or just as much) water in both of these glasses, or does one glass have more water?"

Asking for Justifications

Many tasks that reveal children's thinking require that you ask for a justification of the child's answer. There are many ways to do so. Sometimes being asked "why" makes children uncertain of their response, since they may have come to associate the question "why" with being wrong. Rehearse several ways of asking for explanations, such as "What makes you think that?" "How come you think so?"

Avoiding Negative Feedback

When a response is incorrect, avoid saying so. Simply accept it as the child's view of the world. If you feel a need to give feedback, say something like this: "I see what you mean" or "I see how you understand that."

From Berk, L. E. (1996). *Suggestions for observing and interviewing young children.*
© Laura E. Berk, reprinted by permission.

NOTES

NOTES

NOTES

NOTES

NOTES

NOTES

NOTES

NOTES

NOTES

NOTES

NOTES

NOTES

NOTES

NOTES

NOTES

NOTES

NOTES

NOTES

NOTES

NOTES

NOTES

NOTES